WORKBOOK

TRIGGERED TOO

D1603436

CHRIS & RAHNELLA ADSIT

Triggered Too is a film produced by Victor Marx All Things Possible,
a 501(c)3 non-profit corporation.

PO Box 63176
Colorado Springs, CO 80862
info@victormarx.com

Disclaimer:

> This booklet is not a substitute for appropriate medical or psychological care for those experiencing significant emotional pain or whose ability to function at home, school or work is impaired. Chronic or extreme stress may cause a wide assortment of physical and psychological problems. Some may require evaluation and treatment by medical or mental health professionals. When in doubt, seek advice from a professional.

All Scripture quotations, unless otherwise indicated, are taken from *The Holy Bible, New International Version*®, NIV®. Copyright © 1973, 1978, 1984, 2011 by Biblica, Inc.®. Used by permission. All rights reserved worldwide.

Other versions of The Bible used are:

NAS: *New American Standard Bible.* Copyright © 1960, 1962, 1963, 1968, 1971, 1972, 1973, 1975, 1977, 1995 by the Lockman Foundation. Used by permission.

NLT: *Holy Bible*, New Living Translation. Copyright © 1996, 2004, 2015 by Tyndale House Foundation. Used by permission of Tyndale House Publishers Inc., Carol Stream, Illinois 60188. All rights reserved.

NKJV: New King James Version®. Copyright © 1982 by Thomas Nelson. Used by permission. All rights reserved

ISBN: 978-164370729-7

Printed in the United States of America

TABLE OF CONTENTS

SOUND FAMILIAR?

Can you identify with some (or all) of these statements from trauma sufferers in the film?

- I couldn't control my emotions.
- I could not maintain normal relationships.
- I wouldn't be able to go to sleep; I was just paralyzed.
- I suffered abuse at the hands of my step-father: physically, emotionally, and even sexually.
- I was tortured, left for dead.
- God please, give me one more day with my husband. Please, please don't take him.
- I just couldn't believe it was real.
- I really wanted to end my life. It made a lot of sense to me, to just go to heaven.
- I'd always associated PTSD with military people, or grownups – certainly not a child.
- I couldn't figure out how to survive in society because of my emotional issues.

It doesn't have to *stay* like this.

> *"So many people who have PTSD, given the right help in a biological, psychological, social, spiritual way can get dramatically better."*
> —Dr. Daniel Amen, Psychiatrist,
> brain health expert

> *"We really are made to heal. I am amazed at what people can heal from."*
> —Dr. Arlys McDonald,
> Clinical Psychologist

A COMPLEX –
YET SIMPLE – TRUTH

You have approximately 100 trillion cells in your body. Each one is equipped to carry out a specific purpose in concert with all your other cells, tissues, and organs. And when they are harmed, each cell has been designed to shift gears and make "unit healing" their top priority.

Which begs the question: how could such order, unity, and brilliance have come from such incredible complexity?

The film you have watched has probably opened your eyes regarding the effects your own trauma has had on you. It named it and defined it. Now – what do you do about it?

Victor and Eileen Marx – and many other millions of people who have experienced victory and healing from PTSD – would tell you that the primary factor in their healing is God.

You may not have heard God mentioned a lot in the film, but they want you to know the whole story. We really are designed with amazing resiliency, and the One who energizes and orchestrates the incredibly complex healing process is our Creator – who made us and knows us inside and out.

According to a Pew Research survey conducted in late 2017, 80% of Americans believe in God. But what do they believe? When they believe He is a loving, all-knowing, and all-powerful God, they find that they can go to Him with their wounds, difficulties, and afflictions to find help and healing.

There is a growing trend within psychology that recognizes the importance of including spirituality in the therapy of emotional problems. Actually, this trend has its roots in the founder of analytical psychology, Carl Jung, who stated that all of his patients over the age of 35 who did not develop a spiritual orientation to life were never healed.[1]

Today, even secular authorities are recognizing that dealing with trauma and its effects must include not only the physical and psychological components, but also the spiritual. The American Psychological Association now publishes a quarterly journal called "Spirituality in Clinical Practice." The Veterans Administration has launched a nationwide training program to counter PTSD called "Building Spiritual Strength." These are serious endorsements regarding the need for the spiritual element in the healing of trauma.

Where do you stand? Are you among the 80% who are willing to consider God as your partner in healing?

Or are you skeptical? What have you tried so far in your pursuit of relief from your trauma symptoms? If what you've been trying hasn't worked, why not try something different?

This booklet offers something different – ways to connect with God, "The Healer," to return you to a place of strength and stability. We urge you to take it seriously.

CHAPTER 1

WHAT IS NORMAL?

"I tell my patients that 'Normal' is nothing more than a setting on a dryer or a city in Illinois."

—Dr. Daniel Amen

Those who experience trauma symptoms are not weak, cowardly, or crazy. They are *wounded*. And wounds can heal if proper measures are taken.

Just as it's *normal* to bleed when you get cut, and *normal* to experience pain and distraction when you break a bone, it is *normal* to be affected negatively by traumatic incidents. It is *normal* to be shaken when you are assaulted, raped, injured, or kidnapped, or when you view horrific acts and atrocities. It would be *abnormal* if a person *wasn't* affected by these things. It shows that a person is human, and that when they or others experience trauma, it matters.

But post-traumatic stress <u>disorder</u> (PTSD) is *not* normal. It is very *common,* but none of us feels it's normal. After Becky lost her little boy due to that accident and began to realize that ending her life and going to heaven to care for him began to make sense to her, she knew this thinking was not *normal*. When Frank started his MMA career after a very abusive childhood, he began to figure out that his mindset in the ring was not *normal*. At any given time, eight million

Americans are struggling with PTSD. Among the non-military, non-first-responder community, this would include more than 4 out of 100 men and 10 out of 100 women.[2] Common, but not normal.

Everyone who encounters trauma experiences post-traumatic stress. But when a person gets stuck in that high-alert, defensive mode, when visions of the trauma keep a person up night after night, when annoyances ramp up to explosive rage in seconds, when a person in Suburbia is convinced that they could be attacked at any moment, and all this hangs on for weeks, months or years, this is not normal.

> *"PTSD is an imbalance in the brain, where the brain gets stuck – either on the one side: fight or flight, or on the other side: a freeze response. We all go through traumas in life. If the trauma is too great, the brain responds to it to keep the individual alive. But in keeping the individual alive, it often thinks that's the pattern it needs to hold on to. It gets stuck in that asymmetry. And therefore, we generally call that Post-traumatic Stress Disorder."*
>
> —Lee Gerdes, Founder & CEO
> of Brain State Technologies

However...

- This is not weakness.
- This is not cowardice.
- This is a *wound*.
- And as Victor and all the others who spoke on the film found out, this wound can be healed.

If you're cut, you don't want to *keep* bleeding. You don't want a broken bone to go unset. So you take steps to deal with these issues. In the same way, no one wants to stay in that high-stress, high-alert PTSD mode.

Though a person does not have to *stay* stuck, there are components of PTSD that will hobble your efforts to get un-stuck. See if you can identify with these competing issues:

You need to talk to receptive, understanding friends and professionals about your trauma...	PTSD will crank up your anxiety every time you try.
You need to get some consistent sleep...	PTSD will wake you up with nightmares.
You need to stay involved with life, hang with good, optimistic friends...	PTSD will make you want to isolate.
You need to set goals, move forward, accomplish things...	PTSD will shift you into neutral, take away your ambition, keep you in the past.

So, no one is saying it's easy — in fact, it can be a real fight. But it's good for any fighter to be aware of his or her enemy's tactics and the terrain on which the battle must be fought. You are gaining awareness. And you also should draw upon the <u>assets</u> you have:

- **God**, who created you, and wants to heal you.
- **The Bible**, which will bring truth to counter the lies of hopelessness, strength to counter the wounds of your trauma, and transformation to counter your immobility.
- **Fellow fighters**, who understand what you're going through, and will fight with you.
- **Family and friends**, who may not understand all

you've experienced but want to walk with you and provide support though the dark valleys.

- **Counselors**, who know how to deal with PTSD.

- **Doctors**, who will help you address the physical aftermath of your trauma.

- **Mentors and pastors**, who will care for, encourage, and counsel you regarding spiritual issues.

- **Exercise**, which will keep your heart, lungs, brain, guts, muscles, and nervous system working better, and help your hormonal imbalances stabilize.

- **Community resources**, which can help you move forward with employment, education, therapy, recreation, household needs, financial help, etc.

- **Opportunities to serve**, which will get your focus off yourself, break you loose from the anchors that may be holding you back, and transfer optimism to those less fortunate.

These are *all* in your inventory of allies, tactics, and weapons. But allies who are not accessed can't help. Tactics that are not executed are worthless. Weapons that remain in the armory won't defend.

PTSD is not *normal.* But it can be beaten, if you'll fight.

CHAPTER 2

IDENTIFYING THE INVISIBLE ENEMY

"I'm so grateful that we found the right doctor who looked at me and said, 'You have PTSD.' This is an invisible enemy I can attack and hit the target, and feel better – finally."

—Victor Marx

What is PTSD?

Your trauma didn't just quietly sneak up on you. It came with a horrendous jolt, or several jolts over a period of weeks or months. Something exploded. You were attacked. There was an accident. You saw something horrifying that you never thought you'd see. Someone around you died. Maybe you almost did too.

At the moment of crisis, these physical and psychological shocks rattle our brain and temporarily alter the way it reacts and responds to lesser threats. There are good reasons why this happens:

- The reactive, emotional, alarm-triggering right side of our brain temporarily overwhelms the logical, analytical, practical left side of our brain so that we can respond quickly to address the threat and survive.

- If this didn't happen, we might burn precious seconds while our left brain analyzes the situation, files the incoming information into neat categories, ponders the philosophy of why this incident is occurring, and we end up dead. Instead, the right brain shouts, "LESS THINKING! MORE ACTION!"

• If the threat isn't neutralized soon, our lower brain takes over. It is in charge of all automatic functions in your body: breathing, heartbeat, digestion, etc. Guess what else is automatic? Staying alive. If this is in question, the lower brain takes over and pops off an amazing cascade of hormones.

• Strength, speed, endurance, and focus ramp up. It's live-or-die time. Instantly we are ready to fight, fly or freeze like we never have before. We will eliminate *anything* that tries to keep us from ending the threat and/or getting to safety.

• Meanwhile, our right brain is recording vivid pictures and video of the event, probably so that we will remember it, and avoid it in the future.

There are two things you need to know about this:

1. God gave us this reactive pathway so that we could do whatever was necessary to survive. God knows that when our minds or bodies are threatened, this behavior needs to come out or we could die.

2. No matter how hard we might have tried, we couldn't have stopped this reaction. We can't stop our heartbeat by thinking about it. Neither can we fully control our actions when our brain has clicked into this mode.

About 75% of all Americans have experienced at least one traumatic event in their lives strong enough to trigger Post-traumatic Stress Disorder. Most people can process the trauma in a short period of time (hours, weeks, a few months) and return to relative normalcy. The idea is, after the threat has passed we need to allow the temporarily-suppressed analysis and emotional responses to surface, address them, bring them into our present mindset, properly file them in our minds, learn from them, and move on.

But if memories of the event are not processed, our mind gets confused. *"Is this a memory, or is this happening NOW and I need to react?"*

If we continue to suppress these poorly-filed memories, eventually our mind and body are no longer content to let the incident slide, and they demand action.

So we start having symptoms – ghosts of the ones we had during the actual trauma. Or we do things our mind thinks we *must* do in order to stay safe "...until we can figure all this out."

Later, whenever our brain senses that it's in – or about to enter – a similar threatening scenario because of some sensory trigger (a smell, a sound, a sight, a memory), it quickly opens up the media files it created during the earlier traumatic event and puts on an intense slide and video show to remind us that we don't want to go there again. There may be no *actual* threat, but our right brain once again screams, "Threat! React! Fight! Run!"

PTSD Defined

Post-traumatic Stress Disorder is a condition that exhibits characteristic symptoms following exposure to a traumatic event or series of events in the following contexts:[3]

1. **Direct exposure** to a traumatic event(s) such as war, threatened or actual assault or sexual violence, robbery, childhood physical abuse, kidnapping, torture, terrorism, natural disaster, severe vehicle accident, etc.

2. **Witnessing** a traumatic event(s) in person.

3. **Indirect exposure** by learning that a close relative or close friend experienced a violent or accidental traumatic event.

4. **Repeated or extreme indirect exposure to horrific details** of traumatic event(s) in the course of professional duties (e.g. collecting body parts, repeatedly exposed to detailed reports of child abuse, etc."

PTSD Symptoms

God has made our brains amazingly complex (which you would expect of an organ composed of 120 billion neurons). Different people respond differently to stress and trauma. However, over the years researchers have been able to identify certain common symptoms that are frequently noted in PTSD sufferers. No one has *all* the symptoms, but they will have a unique mixture from four major categories:

1. **Intrusion** (or Re-experiencing) – Memories and images of the traumatic events may spontaneously intrude into our minds, causing intense or prolonged distress or physiological reactions. They can be so vivid we might believe the trauma is reoccurring.

   ❏ Nightmares

   ❏ Sleepwalking; sleep fighting

   ❏ Unwanted daytime memories, images, thoughts

   ❏ Flashbacks

   ❏ Fixation on the event, living in the past

   ❏ Panic attacks

   ❏ Spontaneous dissociative episodes

   ❏ Phobias

2. **Avoidance** – We attempt to avoid any situation, people, or events that remind us of our trauma. We feel numb, emotionless, withdraw into ourselves.

❑ Intentionally avoiding anyone, any place, or anything that reminds us of the traumatic event

❑ Physical/emotional reaction to things that remind us of the traumatic event

❑ Self-isolating; dread of social interaction

❑ Anxiety in crowds, traffic

❑ Very reluctant to talk about our traumatic event

❑ Substance abuse to "numb" ourselves

3. Cognitions and Mood Alterations – Profound negative changes in how we view ourselves and the world.

❑ Reduced cognitive ability (slow thinking, confusion, poor problem-solving, poor memory)

❑ Inability to recall key features of the traumatic event

❑ Persistent, negative trauma-related emotions (fear, horror, anger, guilt, shame)

❑ Persistent, negative distorted self-image ("I am bad.")

❑ Persistent, negative distorted view of the world ("The world is always dangerous.")

❑ Persistent, distorted blame of self or others for causing the traumatic event

❑ Lack of interest or motivation regarding employment, recreation, hobbies, sex, exercise

❑ Relationships that were once close are now strained, cold, distant; feeling detached, estranged

❏ Neglect/abandon personal care, hygiene, nutrition

❏ Emotional numbness, flat, can't get happy or sad

❏ Inability to trust others

4. Arousal and Reactivity Alterations – Always on the alert, ready to address a threat and fight at a moment's notice.

❏ Anger, irritability, "short fuse," fits of rage

❏ Hypervigilance, always need to be armed with knife or gun

❏ Easily startled, react to loud noises, jumpy

❏ Substance abuse to "un-numb" ourselves

❏ Trouble falling asleep or staying asleep, night sweats

❏ Accelerated heart rate, respiration, heart palpitations for no reason

❏ Physical fatigue, always tired

❏ Question/abandon faith; feeling betrayed or abandoned by God; mad at God

❏ Becoming violent; provoking fights

❏ Homicidal thoughts

❏ Suicidal thoughts, attempts

❏ Anniversary reactions

❏ Adrenaline junkie

❏ Self-mutilation, cutting, excessive tattooing

Trauma Spectrum

When a person experiences a traumatic event, it doesn't mean that they will immediately zip up into full-blown PTSD. Reactions to trauma can lie anywhere along a spectrum of intensity and duration.

MILD				**SEVERE**
Transitional Stress	Occupational Stress Reactions	Adjustment Disorders	Acute Stress Disorder	PTSD

But here's a rule of thumb: the further you are to the Mild end of the spectrum, the more likely you will experience healing without too much trouble over time. But the further you are to the Severe end, the more likely you will continue to drift that direction unless you become intentional about getting help.

> "All of us have traumatic events in our lives, some very minor, and those reactions we would call Post-traumatic Stress. An earthquake happens, and everyone will have Post-traumatic Stress. But they quickly get through it, generally, and so it doesn't move into a prolonged, more serious symptomatology – which would be Post-traumatic Stress _Disorder_."
>
> —Dr. Arlys McDonald

Which of the symptoms listed in this chapter concern you the most?

_____

_____

_____

_____

_____

_____

_____

_____

_____

_____

_____

_____

_____

_____

_____

_____

CHAPTER 3

FIVE OTHER GATEWAYS

"There is such a stigma about what PTSD is, and it's really an information storage issue. It causes mental health problems and symptoms, but you don't get PTSD because you are mentally ill or broken, or did a wrong action, or anything like that. You get PTSD because you are a human being, and the way that our bodies respond to threat causes it to be stored differently."

—Dr. Carrie Elk

There are always several ways a person can enter a house. The front door may be the most frequent way, but you can gain access through various windows, back doors, through the cellar, or even tearing off part of a roof.

And there are several ways that trauma can gain access to our lives besides the typical ones mentioned in the previous chapter, which we would call "**Critical Incident Trauma**." They enter in ways different from PTSD, but their effects and symptoms are very similar. However, this doesn't mean that they are resolved in similar ways, so it's good to know the difference.

1. Traumatic Brain Injury (TBI)

This is a physical injury to the brain as the result of a concussive impact. There are three types of TBIs:

- **Closed-skull injury:** The force of a powerful blow to the head, whiplash, or an explosion can launch the brain on an internal collision course with the skull. Result: an injured brain inside an intact skull, and no outward signs of physical injury.

- **Open-skull injury:** A projectile, such as a bullet, shrapnel, or fragment of a fractured skull penetrates the brain, causing bruising and bleeding.

- **Blast-Induced TBI**: The shock wave released by an explosion can pass through a person's body and brain dozens of yards away, damaging neurons, blood vessels, and organs. Again, no outward signs of physical injury.

A very difficult aspect of TBI has to do with diagnosis. Unless there is an open-skull injury, there may be no physically-observed reason to suspect a TBI. The symptoms are very similar to PTSD, except for the following ones which are *not* part of a PTSD diagnosis:

- Headaches
- Nausea
- Dizziness/vertigo
- Balance problems
- Ringing in ears
- Difficulty reading
- Visual disturbances
- Lack of forethought
- Obsessive/compulsive
- Inflexible in thought
- Sensitivity to light, touch, sound
- Gets lost often
- Slowed motor skills
- Speech problems
- Seizures
- Losing sense of taste or smell

There are ways to diagnose TBI medically. However, treatment of TBI is not very advanced. It's important to note that, because it is a physical injury, the treatment of TBI is different from the treatment of PTSD.

A person may be diagnosed as having PTSD, when in fact he/she may have TBI, or may have both.

Both Victor and Frank described childhoods that involved severe physical abuse from their fathers or step-fathers. They probably experienced both TBI and PTSD. It's difficult to determine where one leaves off and the other starts.

2. Cumulative Stress

A person may not be able to identify a specific traumatic incident in their life, and yet have the same symptoms of someone who has. They may think, "How can this be? It's bogus for me to feel this way!"

Not true. Symptoms in those who have never been in a "Critical Incident" and yet have lived long-term in a stressful environment can be identical and just as severe as those that develop in an assault victim. This happens as a result of frequent and chronic exposure to stress-producing incidents over an extended period of time. It accumulates.

- Woman married to a violent drunk, who hasn't hit her (yet) but throws things and puts his fist through walls.

- Boy or girl who goes to a school populated by bullies, whom he/she tries to avoid all day every day.

- Worker whose boss threatens to fire him every time his work isn't perfect.

- Young father working two or three jobs – with insufficient sleep – just trying to provide for his family.

- Woman who works in an office where there is constant social back-stabbing and criticism by co-workers.

The stress builds over months or years, and if it isn't dealt with, the body and mind respond as it would to any threat.

Long-term burdensome assignments, exhausting work tempo, inadequate or interrupted sleep, on-going conflicts with fellow workers or bosses, stressful situations at home, rapid technological advances, position insecurity, and increased responsibilities can all contribute to the break-down in a person's resiliency.

3. Derivative Stress

This is a non-medical term that describes strong, long-lasting emotional reactions which derive their impact from trauma that didn't directly happen to them, but happened to another person. There are three types:

- **Secondary Traumatic Stress** – A negative emotional response when something traumatic happens to another person you deeply care about, or when their symptoms negatively affect you, generating similar symptoms in you.
- **Burnout** – The physical, mental and emotional exhaustion experienced by someone who cares for those in great need for extended periods, usually in a high-stress environment.
- **Compassion Fatigue** – When the empathy and compassion one feels for those suffering from the consequences of traumatic events gets overloaded, resulting a pervasive negative attitude, feelings of self-doubt, and a desire to quit or flee.

4. Moral Injury

This growing area of research spotlights a condition caused by committing, failing to prevent, witnessing, or learning about acts that transgress one's deeply held moral beliefs. This may include participating in or witnessing inhumane or cruel actions, failing to prevent the immoral acts of others, as well as engaging in subtle acts or experiencing reactions that, upon reflection, transgress one's moral code. It could involve:

- Betrayal (leaders or bosses who fail you, betrayal by peers or trusted friends)
- Failure to live up to one's own moral standards (lying, stealing, having an affair)
- Disproportionate violence (violently overreacting to an offense, acts of revenge)
- In the military or among first responders:
  - Incidents involving civilians (destruction of civilian property, assault)
  - Within-rank violence (taking part in military sexual trauma, friendly fire, fragging)

The symptoms of Moral Injury can appear very similar to PTSD or TBI – again, complicating the diagnosis. Here are some of the classic symptoms of MI:

- Loss of meaning
- Guilt/shame
- Loss of sense of reliability of the world
- View themselves as bad
- Sense of worthlessness
- Abandonment of previously held moral values
- Abandonment of faith or religious practices
- Emotional distance from friends and family
- Withdrawal from communication
- Distrust of authority
- Self-sabotage
- Self-harm

Here are two significant differences between MI and PTSD:

1. MI is a <u>guilt/shame response</u> to a transgression; PTSD is a <u>fear response</u> to danger, stress, and trauma.

2. In MI, I see myself as the <u>perpetrator</u>, the one who killed, injured, or failed to prevent injury; in PTSD, I see myself as the <u>victim</u>, the one targeted or injured.

According to recent studies, intense feelings of guilt is a very significant predictor of both suicide attempts and suicide preoccupation.[4] If this is something that you struggle with, don't minimize it! It is *vital* that you not only take this to God, but that you also take it to a trusted counselor – especially one who has been trained in dealing with Moral Injury.[5]

5. Previous Childhood Trauma

> *"I had a father who didn't claim me as his kid, my mother was married six times, I was in 14 schools, 17 houses... I suffered abuse at the hands of my step father physically, emotionally, and even sexually – everything from water dunking, to being electrocuted or shocked, left for dead in a commercial cooler, and it was enough to make my mind really break."*
>
> —Victor Marx

In the film, Victor, Frank, Theresa, and Andrea each shared that the stress and trauma reactions they have experienced later in life have their roots in broken homes and abusive childhoods. It's much more common than you might think.

When a child experiences trauma at the hands of someone he/she should be able to trust and depend on, disruptions occur in the development of their bodies and minds.

All of us were born with a very effective stress response system. When a child senses a threat, this system dumps high doses of adrenalin and cortisol into their bloodstream to get them ready to fight or run away. But if they are unable to defend themselves or escape from an abusive family dynamic, many children are forced to shut down with their body still full of chemicals and employ the freeze response. The brain often stores the memories of these experiences improperly, and if this happens repeatedly, the pathway by which the child's developing brain deals with threat is altered in harmful ways.

The effects of this is often retained into adulthood, causing the person to have amplified emotional and physical responses to threat and danger. Present day events may trigger strong feelings that really belong to an incident in the past, tapping into a deep well of feelings whose sources remain elusive.[6]

A landmark study of over 17,000 adults was conducted in 1995-1997 by the Centers for Disease Control and Kaiser Permanente.[7] The study concluded that if a person experiences childhood abuse, the probability that they will experience depression, PTSD, suicidal ideation, and health problems as an adult is significantly increased.

The study identified several "Adverse Childhood Experiences" (ACEs). They include:

- Physical abuse or neglect
- Emotional abuse or neglect
- Sexual abuse
- Violence between parents
- Parents who were separated or divorced
- Household members who were substance abusers, mentally ill, suicidal, or incarcerated

Compared to a person with zero ACEs, a person who had experienced four or more ACEs is four and a half times more likely to develop depression as an adult, and twelve times more likely to have suicidal ideation.

The Way Out

So many of the difficulties that feed our trauma symptoms have to do with *memories*. It's not so much the incident itself that generates stressful reactions, but our perception of or reaction to the event – and how we remember it.

There are three basic types of memory:

- **Procedural memory** – learned activities that we do automatically, like walking, riding a bike, tying a shoe, or spelling "cat."

- **Semantic memory** – involves remembering concepts, words, facts, data, and other bits of knowledge, trivia, etc., like quoting the Lord's prayer or the Pledge of Allegiance.

- **Episodic memory** – memory of an event that occurred in our lives, usually engaging the senses, including images, feelings, behaviors and meaning, like "Remember the time we went body-surfing in Hawaii?" "Remember when we were in that car accident?"

Traumatic soul wounds are episodic memories – very negative ones, in dire need of processing and integration into our lives, values, beliefs and sense of well-being. The best way to lessen the impact of a negative episodic memory is with a more powerful *positive* episodic memory.

How do you remember your traumatic events? For many people, one glaring omission in their memories often has to do with God's presence. Where was He? Why did He allow this to happen to me?

Let's look at this issue, and make a memory...

CHAPTER 4

WHERE WAS GOD?

Some of the strongest, most faith-filled, godly people in history have asked this question. Even Jesus Christ cried out from the cross…

My God! My God! Why have You forsaken Me?
—Matthew 27:46

When a person experiences a horrific event, when evil seems to triumph, when the innocent are harmed, when a random, unexpected event results in destruction and death, it is a natural human tendency to ask, "Where was God? If He is all-powerful and loving, why didn't He prevent this?"

This line of inquiry is natural, and *normal*. So what's the answer?

Free Will

One of the foundational characteristics of God repeated throughout the Bible is that He loves us. A corollary of this characteristic is that He has given us free will and will not violate it. He won't force you to do anything. He didn't make a planet of puppets who will do His bidding when He pulls the right strings. Because He loves you, what He wants more than anything in the universe is *your* love, sent back to Him of your own free will. If we are forced, it's not love at all. It's *physics*: simple action and reaction.

Love Rejected

"We do not want this man to reign over us!"

That's from a story Jesus told in Luke 19 about how He was going to be rejected as King. The story came true a few days later.

"Away with Him! Away with Him! Crucify Him! We have no king but Caesar!"

The people didn't want God – or His Son – as their ruler, so they killed Him. But this was nothing new. People have been rejecting God's rule in their affairs since the beginning of time. Mankind said, "No" to God at the first opportunity, and we have been saying "No" ever since – as a species, as nations, and as individuals.

God reaches out to each one of us and asks, "May I be your Shield, your Guide, your Guardrails, your Sustainer, your Companion, your Comforter?" And every one of us at one time or another has replied, "Nice idea, but no. I would rather do as I please."

God didn't change His mind about respecting our free will. He granted our wish. He backed off. But not very far. He's always there, always ready to respond, always reaching out – but out of our way. "We don't need Him. We can handle things just fine by ourselves."

How are we doing?

Consider just the last half of the 20th century. After the Nazis exterminated six million Jews and six million Christians and gypsies in concentration camps during WWII, the world vowed, "We will *never* let that happen again!"

However...

- Between 1958 and 1961, Mao Zedong orchestrates the starvation deaths of at least 20 million Chinese.

- In 1972 intake ducts in the dams of the Nile are plugged with the bodies of more than 300,000 Ugandans whom Idi Amin murdered with impunity.

- Between 1975 and 1978 Pol Pot executes two million of his own Cambodian people.

- In 1984, Saddam Hussein gasses thousands of Kurdish families in northern Iraq.

- During three months in 1994, over a million Hutus and Tutsis hack each other to death in Rwanda and Burundi.

- In 2001, Osama bin Laden orchestrates an attack on the World Trade Center, killing 2,977 people.

- In 2009 Boko Haram rises in Nigeria. 15,000 have been killed, more than two million displaced.

- In 2011 civil war breaks out in Syria. So far, over 500,000 have died, 11 million have fled their homes.

- In 2014 ISIS rises, killing thousands, enslaving thousands, and forcing more than 1.3 million to flee.

- In 2014, Russia attacks Ukraine in a land-grab. So far, over 10,000 have died and 1.6 million are homeless.

More innocent men, women and children were murdered through genocide in the 20th century than have been killed in all the previous wars in history combined. And as this carnage spreads and defines the modern world, men continue self-assured at the helm, and are mostly not inter-ested in God's help.

And here's the irony: we tell God to get lost, then blame *Him* for our unimaginable inhumanity toward each other.

As one Auschwitz prisoner remarked bitterly to his friend, "Where is God?" The other, pondering their sadistic guards and the unresponsive world, replied, "Where is man?"[8]

You may be thinking the same thing. "Where was God when I experienced my trauma?"

The answer is: He was right there with you, though you couldn't see Him, ready to act in a way and at a time that is often hard to understand in the heat of the moment. He wept over your losses, and over the other victims around you – just as He did at the tomb of His dead friend Lazarus. He is biding His time until the day He will judge and elimi-nate all evil and those who practice it. But in the meantime – right now – He is walking beside you and anguishing over the pain you are experiencing. And He wants to help.

The Redeemer

This may or may not have occurred to you, but even if you were injured or wounded, you lived. And if you'll let Him, He will factor that great trauma into your present and future, and bring *good* out of it. He redeemed Lazarus from the tomb; He can redeem your traumatic experiences too.

As you let Him open your eyes to His presence in the midst of your crisis, you'll receive a more powerful episodic memory that will eclipse the previous one, and help bring healing.

The Bible says that God put eternity in our hearts (Eccle-siastes 3:11). Because of this, we *know* there's something beyond this crazy life. We *long* for it. It makes us conclude in our hearts and minds that death is so *unnatural,* and the present evil and suffering are *not right;* yet we are utterly immersed in it.

How can we gain His perspective? How can we heal? That's what the rest of this booklet is about.

> *"One of the things that builds hope is insightful awareness. So if you understand your problem, if you understand that there's a normal trajectory and cycle to your problem, you're going to be more hopeful in response to that problem."*
>
> —Dr. David Rudd;
> President of University of Memphis

Write out your trauma story. What impact did your trauma have on you? Where was God during your traumatic event(s)? Where is He now?

_____

_____

_____

_____

_____

_____

_____

My trauma story (continued).

CHAPTER 5

ELEMENTS OF A HEALING ENVIRONMENT

God is the great Healer (Exodus 15:26). Sometimes He heals by a direct, miraculous touch. But more often He prompts us to remove harmful impediments and damaging factors in our lives, and to add factors that will optimize the healing principles He has put in each of us to heal physically, mentally, and spiritually. In this second half of the booklet, we'll briefly examine these healing elements:

- Connecting With God
- The Bible
- Prayer
- Community
- Dealing with Loss (Grief)
- Forgiving Others
- Forgiving Yourself
- Service
- Mindset

Element Selection

Can you pick and choose which to include? Sure. But it depends on your objective: status quo, or Post-traumatic Growth?

We all have a general idea of what it takes to grow a field of corn. We need good ground relatively free of rocks, nutritious soil, maybe a little fertilizer and pre-emergent pesticide, an irrigation system, water, sunshine, weather that's warm but not too warm, and a way to keep the bugs and birds from eating the crop. We *could* skip a few of those elements, and the corn *could* still grow, but not as well, and without producing as great a crop. The more of those elements we include, the better the end result will be.

It's the same idea with your healing environment. The more of these Healing Elements you include in your life, the quicker and more completely you will heal, and the more pronounced will be your Post-traumatic *GROWTH*.

Defining Terms

What do we mean by "Healing?" What most trauma sufferers want more than anything is for life to go back to how it was prior to their trauma. But the sad truth is: you can't get back there. That bell can't get un-rung.

But it IS possible to get to the place where your trauma symptoms are no longer running your life. It doesn't mean you're symptom-free. It means that YOU are now driving the boat – the boat is no longer driving you.

And it IS possible to get to a place where you have overcome the effects of your trauma to a degree that you can now turn around and help others who are hurting.

And it IS possible to come to a place where God has made you stronger, more resilient, and more resourceful in ways you never were – and never could have been – prior to your traumatic experiences.

CHAPTER 6

HEALING ELEMENT 1:
CONNECTING WITH GOD

"God is the only one who can fulfill that deep void in my soul that I have."

—Andrea

Of all the elements that we could recommend for your Healing Environment, establishing a relationship with God through Jesus Christ is the most powerful.

This goes back to the point about free will. By willingly *choosing* to ask Jesus Christ to come into your life and take His position as your Lord and Savior, this opens up the conduit of healing like nothing else we have seen. He won't barge His way in, but He will respond to your invitation.

You may already have established a relationship with God sometime in the past. This may be a good time to re-commit yourself to Him.

But if you have never taken this step before, here are four things to know:

1. God loves you, and created you to have a personal, direct, eternal relationship with Him.

For God so loved the world that He gave His only begotten Son, that whoever believes in Him shall not perish, but have eternal life.

—John 3:16

I have come that they might have life, and have it abundantly.

—John 10:10

What keeps us from experiencing this relationship?

2. Every one of us has individually made the choice to disobey God, separating us from Him.

All have sinned and fall short of the glory of God.

—Romans 3:23

But your iniquities have made a separation between you and your God, and your sins have hidden His face from you so that He does not hear.

—Isaiah 59:2

The word "sin" was originally a Greek archery term, describing the distance between the bullseye on a target, and where the arrow actually hits – thus, the "sin" of the arrow. Even though we may be shooting at God's perfect vision for us, every one of us is missing the mark. "Close" only counts in horseshoes and hand grenades, not before the righteous God of the universe.

Because God is sinless and holy and we have all sinned, there is a great gulf that separates us from Him. Living a "good" life, being religious, or agreeing to a certain set of philosophical propositions all miss the mark, because those actions don't eliminate the root cause of our separation: our sins. Something must be done about *them*.

In this predicament, not only are we missing His direct help in the here-and-now, if we step into eternity in this separated condition, that's the way we'll remain: separated from Him.

3. Jesus Christ is God's only provision for man's sin. Because of His death and resurrection, we can have our sins forgiven, and personally experience God's love, care, and healing.

> **He died in our place**: *God demonstrates His own love toward us, in that while we were yet sinners, Christ died for us.*
>
> —Romans 5:8

> **He rose from the dead**: *Christ died for our sins...He was buried...He was raised on the third day according to the Scriptures...He appeared to Peter, then to the twelve. After that He appeared to more than five hundred...*
>
> —1 Corinthians 15:3-6

The fact that Jesus Christ literally rose from the dead as He said He would – and never again died – validates His claim to be the Son of God, the Messiah, the Eternal King, and the Savior of the world.

> **He is the only way to God**: *Jesus said to him, "I am the way, and the truth, and the life; no one comes to the Father but through Me.*
>
> —John 14:6

4. We must individually receive Jesus Christ into our lives as Lord and Savior. In this way, His sacrificial death applies to our sins, and removes the separation between us and God.

> **We must receive Christ:** *As many as received Him, to them He gave the right to become children of God, even to those who believe in His name.*
>
> —John 1:12

We receive Christ through faith: *By grace you have been saved through faith; and that not of yourselves, it is the gift of God; not as a result of works, so that no one may boast.*
—Ephesians 2:8,9

Receiving Christ isn't like joining a club, switching philosophies, or signing up for an insurance policy. The Bible describes it as being "born again" into the realm of the Spirit of God. We've all been born physically, but we need to be born spiritually too. Read John 3:1-8 to observe Jesus explaining this to Nicodemus, a very religious man. By receiving Christ into your life, you are being born into God's eternal family – a relationship that will never end.

We receive Christ by personal invitation: *[Christ speaking:] Behold, I stand at the door and knock; if anyone hears My voice and opens the door, I will come in to him.*
—Revelation 3:20

Receiving Christ involves turning to God from self (repentance) and trusting Christ to come into our lives, to forgive our sins, and to help us heal and grow. Since it was by an act of our will that we originally became separated from God, it is by an act of our will that we can become reunited.

If you have never done this before – or feel the need to renew your commitment to God – the following is a suggested prayer. What's important is the attitude of your heart, not these specific words...

Lord Jesus, I want to know you personally. Thank you for dying on the cross for my sins. I open the door of my life and receive You as my Savior and Lord. Thank you for forgiving me of my sins and giving me eternal life. Help me heal, and make me the person you want me to be.

If you prayed this prayer and truly meant it from your heart, He has come in! And with Him He has brought His power, insight, direction, and eternal life!

> *[Christ speaking]: Truly, truly, I say to you, he who hears My word, and believes Him who sent Me, has eternal life, and does not come into judgment, but has passed out of death into life.*
> —John 5:24

> *The testimony is this, that God has given us eternal life, and this life is in His Son. He who has the Son has the life; he who does not have the Son of God does not have the life. These things I have written to you who believe in the name of the Son of God, so that you may know that you have eternal life.*
> —I John 5:11-13

My connection story – how I began my relationship with God.

_____

_____

_____

_____

_____

_____

_____

_____

_____

_____

_____

_____

_____

_____

_____

_____

CHAPTER 7

HEALING ELEMENT 2:
THE BIBLE

"Set your hearts to all the words which I testify among you this day... For it is not a vain thing for you, because it is your life."

—Moses, Deuteronomy 32:46,47

We were created as three-dimensional beings: body, mind, and spirit. We know our bodies need to be fed – most people are familiar with hunger pangs. But our minds and spirits need nourishment too. Our minds are usually fed by things like truth, beauty, information, and friendships. Our spirit – the part of us that relates to God – is fed by the words of God: the Bible.

Man shall not live on bread alone, but on every word that proceeds out of the mouth of God.

—Jesus, Matthew 4:4

Like newborn babies, long for the pure milk of the word, so that by it you may grow in respect to salvation.

—1 Peter 2:2

Besides keeping you from starving spiritually, why else is it important for you to spend some time every day feeding your spirit with the Bible? Check these verses...

*Study this Book of Instruction continually. Meditate on it day and night so you will be sure to obey everything written in it. Only then will you **prosper and succeed in all you do**.*

—Joshua 1:8 (NLT)

*The law of his God is in his heart; **his feet do not slip**.*

—Psalm 37:31

*How can a young man **keep his way pure**? By living according to Your word... I have hidden Your word in my heart that I might **not sin against You**.*

—Psalm 119:9,11

*If you hold to My teaching, you are really My disciples. Then you will know the truth, and the truth will **set you free**.*

—John 8:31,32

There are several ways you can feed on God's word. Make sure you engage in all of them, because each one feeds your spirit differently!

HEAR – Listening to a sermon at church or via podcast, attending a Bible study, discussing the Bible with friends.

READ – Like any book. Open you Bible and read a chapter first thing in the morning or whenever you have time.

STUDY – More focused and deeper than just reading. Consulting Bible study aids, cross-referencing, journaling.

MEMORIZE – Committing meaningful verses to memory. This will affect your actions and your reactions.

MEDITATE – Deliberately reflecting on God's word, praying about it, considering how to apply it to your life.

Your Weapon

In Ephesians 6:14-17 the Bible describes our spiritual armor. God's word is called the "sword of the Spirit." A sword is both an offensive and defensive weapon. Jesus used His to great effect in His battle with Satan in the wilderness: Matthew 4:1-11. Read it to see how He used the word.

A soldier who is in a combat zone is intimately acquainted with every square millimeter of his weapon. Why? Because it will keep him alive. Become just as familiar with this spiritual weapon too, for the same reason.

Why I need to study the Bible more and what I plan to do about it.

My Bible study plan (continued).

CHAPTER 8

HEALING ELEMENT 3:
PRAYER

*"Call to Me and I will answer you, and I will tell you
great and mighty things, which you do not know."*
—Jeremiah 33:3

No one knows more about how important communication is than a soldier in battle. He needs it to receive intelligence from command, to coordinate his actions with other units, to request resupply and medical evacuation, and for backup and fire support when his unit is attacked.

In a spiritual sense, we are *all* in a battle. It's not one that involves bullets and bombs, but it is just as deadly — because it involves eternity. If we don't maintain communication with our spiritual command, we will be as vulnerable as platoon deep in enemy territory with dead batteries in our radios.

Prayer is simply communication with God. It doesn't have to be flowery or profound. It doesn't have to be spoken dramatically from a pulpit. It can be as simple as a conversation with a friend, or a text on your phone.

What to pray about.

The Bible is pretty clear that God is very happy for us to pray about *anything* that we want to.

> *Don't worry about anything; instead, pray about everything. Tell God what you need, and thank him for all he has done.*
>
> —Philippians 4:6

Let's get a little more specific about what God wants us to pray about. Here are just a *few*...

Give us this day our daily bread. (Matthew 6:11). This covers your everyday needs: food, clothing, shelter, transportation, employment, medical attention, etc.

In everything give thanks; for this is God's will for you in Christ Jesus (1 Thess. 5:18). Express your gratitude to God, even if a particular event isn't what you'd like.

If we confess our sins, He is faithful and righteous to forgive us our sins and to cleanse us from all unrighteousness (1 John 1:9). When we realize we have disobeyed God and feel His loving conviction, we can come to him in repentance, and He will bring cleansing and relief.

Give ear to my words, O Lord, consider my groaning. Heed the sound of my cry for help, my King and my God, for to You I pray (Psalm 5:1,2). Our pain and distress is nothing new to Him. He wants you to voice your frustration – He can take it! Be honest with Him.

But I want ANSWERS!

God will answer every prayer you pray in faith. Every single one. But remember: since He is God, He gets to decide *how* to answer our prayers. He will answer in one of three ways:

Yes – "I was hoping you'd ask that! Done!"

No – "This would not be good for you. Trust Me."

Wait – "This is good, but not right now. Be patient."

His answers will always be what's best for us, for those around us, and for His Kingdom. And since He is all-knowing, loving, and timeless, He ought to know!

46

CHAPTER 9

HEALING ELEMENT 4:
COMMUNITY

"If you have one person who won't judge you, won't try to fix you, will just listen and be supportive, that's critical in this whole process."

—Victor Marx

When in a war zone, how smart is it to engage the enemy if you're by yourself? Any wonder why they call an individual out alone "sniper bait?"

We mentioned earlier that you are in a legitimate war zone everywhere on planet earth. It's a battle fought in the spiritual realm (Ephesians 6:12,13) and the stakes are significant, even eternal. You have an adversary who has sworn to wipe you out (I Peter 5:8). For these reasons, you need battle buddies. A soldier needs them in combat, and you need them now.

God has set up His Kingdom in a way that requires us to be *not* dependent, *not* independent, but *interdependent*. We draw from and contribute to each other. Just like every cell in our body needs the interaction of other cells around them to sustain life, we need other Christians. Here are a few things we gain from each other:

Iron sharpens iron, so one man sharpens another
—Proverbs 27:17

A blade without a whetstone will eventually become dull and useless. We are meant to keep each other sharp.

> *Two are better than one because they have a good return for their labor. For if either of them falls, the one will lift up his companion. But woe to the one who falls when there is not another to lift him up.*
>
> —Ecclesiastes 4:9,10

There is synergy and safety in numbers.

> *Now we who are strong ought to bear the weaknesses of those without strength and not just please ourselves. Each of us is to please his neighbor for his good, to his edification.*
>
> —Romans 15:1,2

By helping our brothers and sisters in need, we strengthen both them *and* us. No handouts, only a leg up.

What Happens Underground?

Redwood trees are massive and seemingly invulnerable. They can live 4,000 years and grow to a height of 350 feet. You'll see them majestically settled in the harsh environs of western Oregon and California. But do you know where you'll never see them? In open fields by themselves.

God has ordained that redwood trees always grow in groves because they have shallow root systems. This is handy where there is little topsoil, as it is in the coastal mountains where they live. But without deep taproots, how do they keep from being blown over?

Their root systems grow laterally – not down – enabling them to interlace their roots underground, forming a solid platform that stretches for miles. When the storms come howling down from the heights, they remain standing because they hold each other up.

This is an excellent picture of how the Christian community is supposed to be. This is a stormy world, and as a trauma survivor you have seen some terrible storms. We need to get involved in each other's lives, interlace our "roots," and hold each other up during life's tempests.

My plan to connect with a healthier, supportive, more life-giving set of friends.

My community enhancement plan (continued).

CHAPTER 10

HEALING ELEMENT 5:
DEALING WITH LOSS

"My soul weeps because of grief; strengthen me according to your word."

—King David, Psalm 119:28

When a person experiences trauma, there is a strong likelihood that he or she lost something – perhaps many things. An appendage, mobility, eyesight, hearing, health, ambition, optimism, future dreams, convictions about God and the world, friends, loved ones...

Loss is always accompanied by grief. It's the normal process of natural emotions that we experience after losing something or someone we value.

God built the grief response into us for the purpose of mentally, emotionally, and spiritually processing loss-producing events, integrating those events into our altered world, and helping us move on to a state of greater strength, resourcefulness, resilience, and faith.

You can't heal what you can't feel.

When we grieve, we are authentically engaging the emotions that come with loss, rather than stuffing or denying them.

At the soul level, we are expressing that we deeply wish the loss had never occurred. We are protesting the injustice of it all, rather than acting like it was OK with us.

We are facing the impact of the loss head on, absorbing it and eventually mastering it – rather than running from it, deflecting it, or pretending it didn't happen, only to have its effects hit us again and again.

You don't have to go through this alone.

When we experience a traumatic loss, grief is what we *feel.* Mourning is *what we do about it.* It's the action side of grief, the externalizing of our internal pain. Our best plan is to invite Jesus to enter the dark forest of our pain, experience it with us, comfort us in the midst of it, and walk us out the other side of it. He will not be passive during this walk. He's been here before many, many times. He will bring healing.

> *He was despised and forsaken of men, a man of sorrows and acquainted with grief...Surely our griefs He Himself bore, and our sorrows He carried.*
> —Isaiah 53:3,4

> *The Lord is near to the brokenhearted and saves those who are crushed in spirit.*
> —Psalm 34:18

> *Blessed are those who mourn, for they shall be comforted.*
> —Matthew 5:4

God will use your grief.

One last reason why we experience loss and grief: God uses these experiences to make us like Him (compassionate and comforting) and to equip us to help others.

> *Praise be to the God and Father of our Lord Jesus Christ, the Father of compassion and the God of all comfort, who comforts us in all our troubles, so that we can comfort those in any trouble with the comfort we ourselves receive from God.*
> —2 Corinthians 1:3,4

CHAPTER 11

HEALING ELEMENT 6:
FORGIVING OTHERS

"Bear with one another, and forgive each other, whoever has a complaint against anyone; just as the Lord forgave you, so also should you."
—Colossians 3:13

U sually when someone has experienced a trauma that was perpetrated by another person (assault, rape, combat, terrorism, car wreck, etc.), there is a sense of violation. Someone is to blame for this, and someone needs to pay. This energizes our drive for revenge.

In war, the strategy of "fighting fire with fire" works. Meet force with superior force. It's the only language aggressors understand. If they bring tanks, we'll bring Warthogs. If we back off, they fill the vacuum and evil triumphs.

But when it comes to interpersonal relationships, this strategy doesn't work. Fighting fire with fire only yields more fire. It leads to needless escalation of tension and no resolution of the problem. And it makes things worse for *you.*

A Different Strategy

Except when it's warranted to set a backfire, firefighters generally prefer to use a substance that is the opposite of fire: *water*. When we are touched by trauma, and suffer pain and loss at the hand of another (whether accidental or intentional), God has something we can use that is the opposite of revenge – and more effective:

> *Do not be overcome by evil, but overcome evil with good.*
>
> —Romans 12:21

Why forgive those who have wronged me?

1. For your own good.

> *See to it that no one comes short of the grace of God; that no root of bitterness springing up causes trouble, and by it many be defiled.*
>
> —Hebrews 12:15

If you don't deal with poison oak, it will take over acres of fields and forests. You can't just mow it, you need to pull out the roots. Harboring unforgiveness is like this. The bitterness spreads, filling our hearts and isolating us from others. It's ironic that our bitterness doesn't affect the offender – only us! Unforgiveness is like drinking rat poison and waiting for the rat to die.

2. It's a Christ-like Characteristic.

> *Father, forgive them, for they do not know what they are doing.*
>
> —Luke 23:34

Jesus was undergoing the most monstrous, unjust wounding in history. But rather than demand justice, He extended mercy to His killers. He'll help us do that.

3. Unforgiveness blocks God's blessings to you.

If you forgive other people when they sin against you, your heavenly Father will also forgive you. But if you do not forgive others their sins, your Father will not forgive your sins.

—Matthew 6:14,15

We tend to want grace from God, but judgment for those who hurt us. God wants us to apply the same standards to others that we expect from Him. When we do, it facilitates His blessings to us. When we don't, it staunches the flow of His grace and mercy to us.

Who do I need to forgive, and for what? How will this benefit me?

Who will I forgive (continued)?

CHAPTER 12

HEALING ELEMENT 7:
FORGIVING YOURSELF

"I brought him into her life. Looking back, there were telltale signs that there was something wrong with him. But of course, I didn't see them. So yes, I'll always blame myself for that."

—Melinda

There are two kinds of guilt: false guilt and real guilt. In both cases, *you* hold the key to forgiveness and relief.

False Guilt

- **Survivor's guilt** – "I shouldn't have survived when others died." "If I'd suffered more, others might have suffered less."

- **Role guilt** – "It was my responsibility to keep other people safe. Someone was was hurt. Someone died. So I failed at my job. It's my fault."

- **Involuntary fight/flight/freeze** – "I always thought I was so brave, but I just froze in my tracks." "I couldn't stop beating that guy who jumped us. I'm disgusting."

- **By association** – "I'm a police officer; some police officers are abusers; so I am among the abusers."

- **Competency** – "If only I had acted quicker, more skill-fully, smarter, with more discernment – other people wouldn't have been hurt."

- **Lose/lose choice** – "My two young children were splashing in the pond, when suddenly they were in over their heads. I dove down where I last saw them. I found one and dragged him to shore and gave him CPR. But when I went back for the other, I couldn't find him. How can I live with that?"

These scenarios all describe choices where there is *no guilt* as far as the laws of God are concerned. Any sense of guilt is based on false premises which Satan ramps up in our minds. It's normal to feel angry, sad, and frustrated about how things turned out, but don't turn that emotion in on yourself. You aren't meant to take the hit for those very unfair and unfortunate events – so don't.

Recognize False Guilt as illogical and irrational, shine a spotlight on its source (Satan), and ask God to remove it from you. God doesn't mean for you to carry that weight.

Real Guilt

At some point in your life, you may have done some things that were real, definite, no-kiddin' sins – not like the fake ones listed above. Two things to know:

1. If you're feeling guilty about *real* sins, it's because your conscience is sensitive to God's conviction – that's *good!*

2. You're not alone. *All* of us have sinned. Every one of us has done things that were against the laws of God. The good news: it's fixable.

   We all, like sheep, have gone astray, each of us has turned to our own way; and the Lord has laid on Him the iniquity of us all.

   —Isaiah 53:6

Steps to Freedom

1. Confess – Tell God that you agree with His assessment that what you did was wrong. Ask Him to forgive you.

> *If we confess our sins, He is faithful and just and will forgive us our sins and purify us from all unrighteousness.*
> —1 John 1:9

2. Repent – This word means to "turn around and go the other direction." When you see you're driving toward the edge of a cliff, expressing alarm about it isn't enough. Put on the brakes. Don't keep going the same direction.

3. Accountability – Whenever we hold a goal that is very important to us, we always put ourselves into an accountability structure of some sort. That's why we hire teachers, coaches, bosses, policeman, personal trainers, Weight Watchers, etc. We know that if we don't we'll seek the path of least resistance, and not attain our goals. This is true if you desire to not offend in the same manner again. Find someone who can hold you accountable, and help push you toward your goals of pure living.

4. Restitution – This has to do with action you may need to take. It's not enough to say, "Oops, sorry. Blew it. Forgive me," and not own up to the consequences, or repeat the same act again and again. Your action will validate your intention. Pay what you owe.

My Personal Steps to Freedom

- Who do I need to seek forgiveness from?
- What do I need to forgive myself for?
- What false guilt have I been struggling with?
- Who could hold me accountable?
- Do I need to make restitution to anyone?

CHAPTER 13

HEALING ELEMENT 8:
SERVICE

[Jesus speaking:] Whoever wants to be first must be slave of all. For even the Son of Man did not come to be served, but to serve, and to give His life as a ransom for many.

—Mark 10:44,45

In what ways have you been involved in "Service" in your past? Perhaps you were in the military, a teacher, a first responder, a mother, a father, a coach, a counselor, a doctor or nurse, a volunteer of some sort. In a very real sense, you made your life available – your time, your talent, your efforts – to be a ransom for others who needed help. You may have made significant sacrifices. Your acts of service may have brought you to your present traumatized condition. Whatever the case, it is *service* that will help pull you out as well.

Helping others who are hurting provides healing power for those who struggle with their own trauma. Virtually every trauma expert agrees on this. There is something about giving of ourselves to those who are having difficulties that empowers us, takes our focus off ourselves, and energizes us.

Two interesting commands.

John 11 gives the report of Jesus raising Lazarus from the

dead. It blew people's minds when Jesus gave the command, *"Lazarus, come out!"* And he did, wrapped in the traditional grave clothes – like 50 Ace Bandages.

The next command Jesus gave relates to you. He said, "Take off his grave clothes and let him go." The One who raised Lazarus from the dead certainly could have also unwrapped him. But he wanted to involve other people in this miracle. By walking up to this dreadful figure, touching him, unwrapping him, and setting him loose, they were being honored by Jesus, and their faith was strengthened.

As a person who has dealt with trauma, you are among the resurrected ones. New life is flowing to you. You've struggled to remove your own grave clothes, or had help removing them, and this has made you profoundly qualified to unwrap the smelly bandages that bind others.

> *To everything there is a season,*
> *A time for every purpose under heaven:*
> *A time to kill, and a time to heal;*
> *A time to break down, and a time to build up.*
> —Ecclesiastes 3:1,3 (NKJV)

In the past, you may have been involved in destructive activities, and you may still hold regrets about that. But that time has passed. A new season has come. It's time to heal, to build up, to unbind the afflicted, and help them heal. It's time for a new kind of heroic, sacrificial service to others.

This not only helps them, but it greatly benefits you, too...

> *If you extend your soul to the hungry and satisfy the afflicted soul, then your light shall dawn in the darkness, and your darkness shall be as the noonday. The Lord will guide you continually, and satisfy your soul in drought, and strengthen*

your bones; you shall be like a watered garden,
and like a spring of water, whose waters do not
fail.

—Isaiah 58:10, 11

It's a beautiful, balancing principle of life: no one can try to help another without helping themselves.

Ways that I can begin serving others.

— Notes & Reflections —

CHAPTER 14

HEALING ELEMENT 9:
MINDSET

"Every morning is a choice. You get up, you pray, you read...

—Andrea

The Army has a plan for helping combat soldiers gain inner strength to face adversity, fear, and hardship with confidence and resolution. It's called *Battlemind Training*. A soldier's mindset is extremely important when it comes to accomplishing the mission and surviving the hazards of war.

In your mission – healing from the effects of trauma – there are certain mindset components vital to creating a healing environment. If they are present, you will heal faster; if not, things will slow and stall. The mindset that God wants to produce in you will include things like faith, hope, love, generosity, humility, and others. All are important, but when it comes to trauma healing three are pivotal. These are components of your *New Battlemind*.

1. Courage

"Courage is not the absence of fear; it is the making of action in spite of fear."

—Dr. M. Scott Peck

If you are human, when you were experiencing your traumatic events you probably experienced fear. You may have froze, and that might have been the best thing to do at the time. But as you are trying to walk out of your dark forest of trauma, to freeze is not to heal. While it's true that every day can provide a new surge of fearful thoughts that threaten to shut you down, healing will come only as you take action. Your trauma symptoms exist *not* because you are weak or cowardly, but because you are wounded, and your brain is not processing incoming stimuli properly. But with God's help, as He instills you with His courage to act despite your fears, you *can* conquer them.

You have problems. We all do. But why should *you* feel any reason to be courageous? Because you are vitally connected to the Supreme Problem-Solver of the Universe. And He says to you the same thing He said to Joshua as he took over as leader of Israel after Moses died:

> *Have I not commanded you? Be strong and courageous. Do not be afraid; do not be discouraged, for the LORD your God will be with you wherever you go.*
>
> —Joshua 1:9

If God has commanded it, it means we have the option of doing it or not. If we choose to do it, He will enable us follow through. He will supply the courage. He will be watching our back the whole way. We *can* step out.

2. Intentionality

As mentioned earlier, trauma is a wound. It's causing you pain and crippling you in some ways. Like any wound, it cannot heal if you simply ignore it. It will fester and get worse. But if you make a plan, make proactive decisions, and do what you know is necessary, the wound can heal.

A person who is in a dangerous situation understands that they need to *take action* if they want to survive. To be passive could mean death – yours, those around you, or whoever you're trying to help. It's also true as you try to break the dangerous bonds of your trauma.

Passivity is a common symptom of trauma. It's easier to shift it into neutral, put on the parking brake and idle. But that strategy won't get you anywhere.

It's good to *start* with courage, but without intentionality you won't *act* on it. They go hand in hand.

King David encouraged his young son Solomon to add intentionality to his courage:

> *Be strong and courageous and <u>get to work</u>. Don't be frightened by the size of the task, for the Lord my God is with you; He will not forsake you. He will see to it that everything is finished correctly.*
>
> —1 Chronicles 28:20

3. Optimism

The fact is, progress toward "healing" for a trauma sufferer is slow and hard. You will have a tendency to focus on your set-backs and stuck-points. You may lie awake at night with accusing thoughts haunting you. "If only I'd done *that!* If only I hadn't done *that!*"

But with God's help, you can start focusing on the *good* things you did, the *right* decisions, the *positive* accomplishments. Your life right now might be characterized by "three steps forward and two steps back." So, focus on the cumulative total. It doesn't matter how many times a football team is behind during the game, it's the final score that counts. The clock is still running for you.

God has promised to bring you through all this as a victor, which is a good basis for *great* optimism:

And we know that in all things God works for the good of those who love Him, who have been called according to His purpose. For those God foreknew He also predestined to be conformed to the image of His Son, that He might be the firstborn among many brothers and sisters. And those He predestined, He also called; those He called, He also justified; those He justified, He also glorified.

—Romans 8:28-30

Notice all the past tense words: foreknew, predestined, called, justified, glorified. All of them are a done deal!

How I can become more courageous, intentional, and optimistic.

CHAPTER 15

HEALING A MARRIAGE IMPACTED BY TRAUMA

By Eileen Marx

"A broken friendship is harder to deal with than a city that has high walls around it."

—Proverbs 18:19

You may be experiencing the pain of a broken friendship in your marriage. Your spouse may seem like he or she is now surrounded with impenetrable walls, separating you from their heart and the closeness you once shared. But please be encouraged by this fact: with God all things are possible, including a healed and whole marriage. I know this from personal experience, and from the experiences of many, many others!

You already know this, but it's still sometimes hard to accept: we humans are not perfect. We *all* need forgiveness and a fresh start. Forgiving someone, especially your spouse for the pain he or she has caused, can be very challenging. Let me share with you what I found to be a very good place to start...

Start by praying for your own heart first and foremost. The chaos, dysfunction, and mistrust can take you to the point of not loving or even liking your spouse. When your heart is hardened, it is very challenging to have feelings of even *wanting* to love again. So start with *you*.

1. What's in *your* heart? Have you ever looked closely at it? Get it all it out. Writing your thoughts on paper or on your computer is a very effective way of thinking deeply and organizing your thoughts about what's swirling around in your heart. Once that is discovered, pray that God would remove anything in you that is contributing to the pain and difficulties in your marriage. Only then will you really be able to begin praying that you could forgive your spouse.

2. Ask God to forgive you for harboring any bitterness or resentment in your heart towards your spouse. Most of all, ask Him to give you His love for him or her so that you can see them in a new light.

3. Start looking for the good. If you call to your mind the good things and resist the temptation to meditate on their negative characteristics, you may start feeling differently again.

4. Get with a trusted friend or family member who can pray with you – and *for* you – during this time. Choose someone you can contact when you feel like you are at your end, someone who will remind you that your marriage is worth the fight.

5. Thank God that this will not last forever and the investment you are making will bring you worthwhile dividends in the end.

We know we have an enemy that works behind the scenes trying to destroy marriages.

Some of the biggest lies the enemy tells a struggling couple are, "Things will never change," or "Your marriage will always be bad." Then he targets our emotions by convincing us with another lie, "You don't love your spouse and you never have," and finishes it off with, "You'd be better off getting a divorce."

But the words of God throw a spotlight on these lies and help us know how to fight what's behind them: "For though we walk in the flesh, we do not war according to the flesh. For the weapons of our warfare are not carnal, but mighty in God for pulling down strongholds, casting down arguments and every high thing that exalts itself against the knowledge of God, bringing every thought into captivity to the obedience of Christ." (2 Corinthians 10:3- 5).

While I didn't fully understand this verse at the beginning of my struggle with my husband's trauma symptoms, I believe the Spirit of God gave me enough understanding to see that this battle encompassed more than just the problems Victor and I were having. With God's help in the battle, we are winning!

My prayers for my spouse (and me!)

Prayers for my spouse and me (continued).

> *"God is able to unscramble eggs. He's able to redeem even the most tragic events and injustices in our lives. We heal. Regardless of the trauma you faced, you were made to heal. So don't give up."*
>
> —Victor Marx

We hope that you found the film *Triggered Too* inspirational and motivating. We also hope that this booklet has given you some insight and direction regarding your efforts to heal from your traumatic events. More work may be required for you. As was the case with Victor and several others who appeared in this film, a good therapist or counselor could be of great benefit. Connecting with a service animal, undergoing EMDR treatment (Eye Movement Desensitization and Reprogramming), using a Hyperbaric chamber, acupuncture, acupressure, "tapping," all these approaches have been shown to be helpful to many people. But as we mentioned, any therapy, treatment, or approach you take will be greatly enhanced if you involve "The Healer" in the process.

Veterans, first responders, or their spouses may be interested in going even deeper using one of these manuals:

NOTES

1. Noam, G.G. & Yehuda, R. (1996). Resilience, vulnerability, and the course of post-traumatic reactions. in B.A. van der Kolk, A.C. McFarlane, & L. Weisaeth (Eds.), *Traumatic Stress: The effects of overwhelming experience on mind, body, and society (pp. 155-181). New York: Guilford Press.*

2. National Center for PTSD. https://www.ptsd.va.gov/public/PTSD-overview/basics/how-common-is-ptsd.asp

3. American Psychiatric Association: *Diagnostic and Statistical Manual of Mental Disorders, Fifth Edition* (DSM-5). Washington, D.C.: American Psychiatric Publishing, 2013). pp. 271-280.

4. Maguen, Luxton, et al. "Killing In Combat, Mental Health Symptoms, and Suidal Ideation in Iraq War Veterans." Journal of Anxiety Disorders, 563-567. Jan, 2011.

5. For a great resource on this subject: Litz, Lebowitz, Gray, Nash. *Adamptive Disclosure – A New Treatment for Military Trauma, Loss and Moral Injury.* Guilford Press, 2016.

6. National Association of Adult Survivors of Child Abuse, online article: "Post Traumatic Stress Disorder in Adult Survivors of Child Abuse," www.naasca.org/2011-Articles/081411-PTSDinAdultSurvivors.htm

7. Dr. Vincent Felitti, Dr. Robert Anda, *et al,* "Relationship of Childhood Abuse and Household Dysfunction to Many of the Leading Causes of Death in Adults," in the American Journal of Preventative Medicine, 1998, Vol. 14, pp 245-258.

8. Os Guiness, *Unspeakable: Facing Up To The Challenge of Evil* (New York: HarperCollins, 2005). p 46.

— Notes & Reflections —

— Notes & Reflections —

— Notes & Reflections —

— Notes & Reflections —

— Notes & Reflections —

— Notes & Reflections —